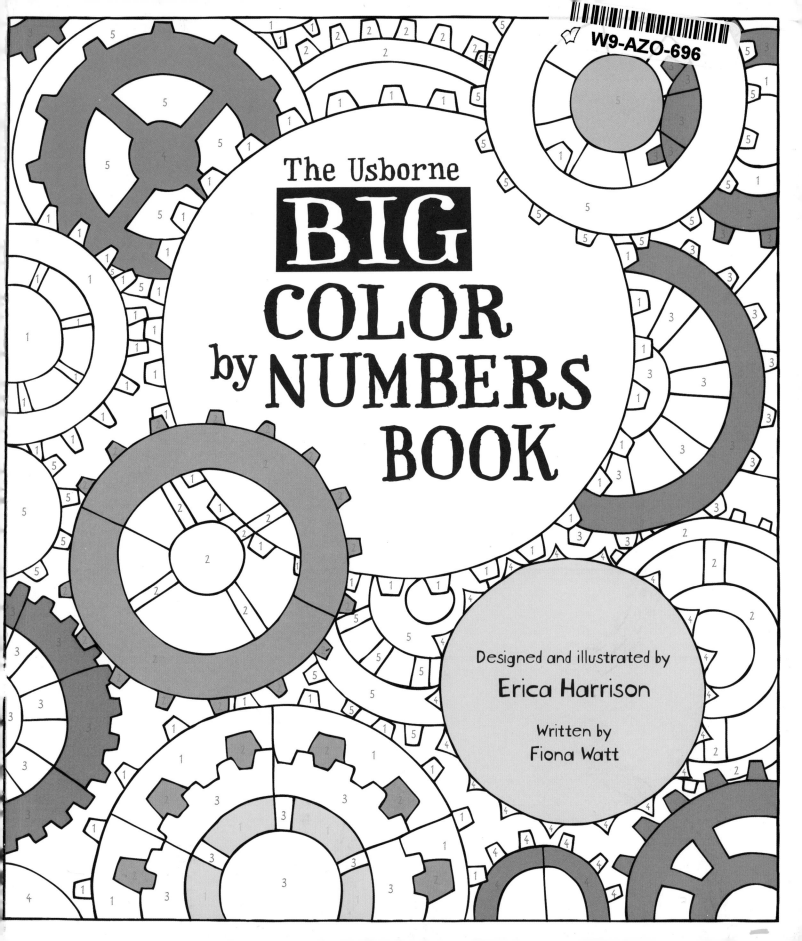

The Usborne
BIG
COLOR
by NUMBERS
BOOK

Designed and illustrated by
Erica Harrison

Written by
Fiona Watt

How to use this book

On most of the pages you will find a number code that shows you which color to use to color in each shape. For example:

1 - blue   2 - orange
3 - yellow   4 - green

Colored spots

Some of the pages use colored spots as guides instead of numbers. Just color in the shape with the same color as the dot inside it.

If you don't have the correct color of pen or pencil, don't worry. Use another color, but remember which number or colored dot represents your new color.

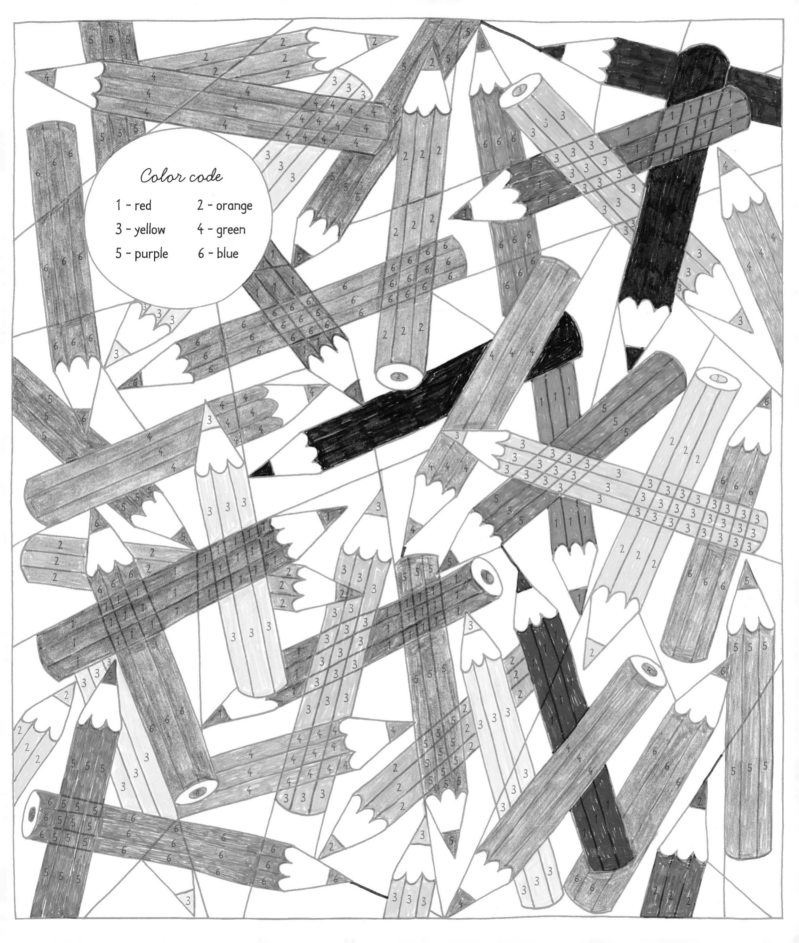

Color code

1 – red   2 – orange
3 – yellow 4 – green
5 – purple 6 – blue

Color code

1 - light blue   2 - dark blue
3 - light gray   4 - dark gray
5 - green   6 - yellow
7 - orange

Color code

1 - pink   2 - yellow
3 - red   4 - purple
5 - orange

Color code

1 - gray   2 - light blue
3 - light green 4 - dark blue
5 - purple

Color code

1 - turquoise   2 - light blue
3 - dark blue   4 - orange

Color code

1 - light green   2 - dark green
3 - yellow   4 - dark blue
5 - pink

Color code

1 – red	2 – light blue	3 – yellow
4 – black	5 – dark blue	6 – green

Color code

1 – yellow

2 – orange

3 – light green

4 – dark green

5 – red

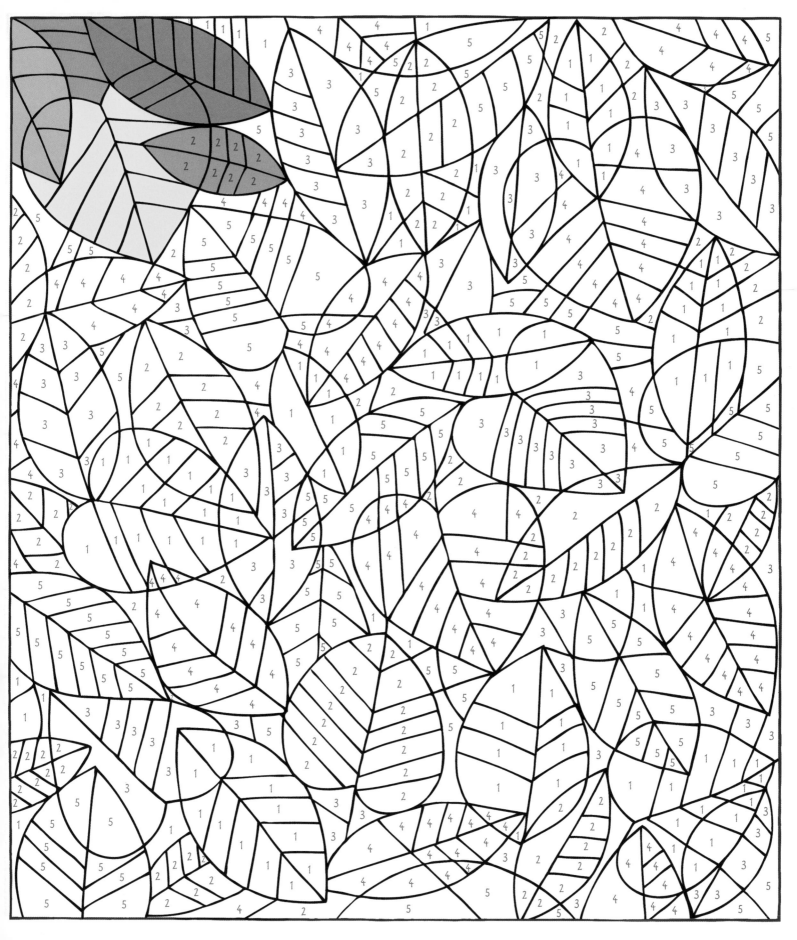

Color code

1 – orange   2 – dark green
3 – yellow   4 – light green
5 – light blue   6 – pink
7 – red

Color code

1 – red   2 – yellow
3 – pink   4 – purple
5 – blue   6 – green
7 – brown

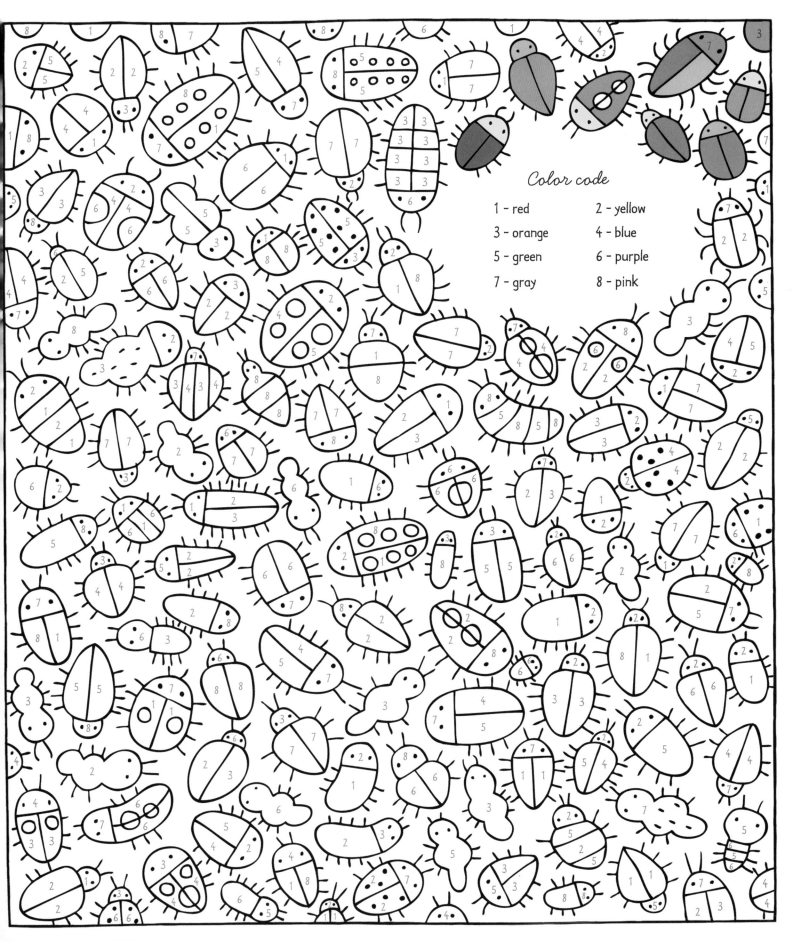

Color code

1 – red   2 – yellow
3 – orange   4 – blue
5 – green   6 – purple
7 – gray   8 – pink

Color code

1 - red   2 - yellow

3 - blue   4 - purple

5 - green   6 - black

7 - pink   8 - orange

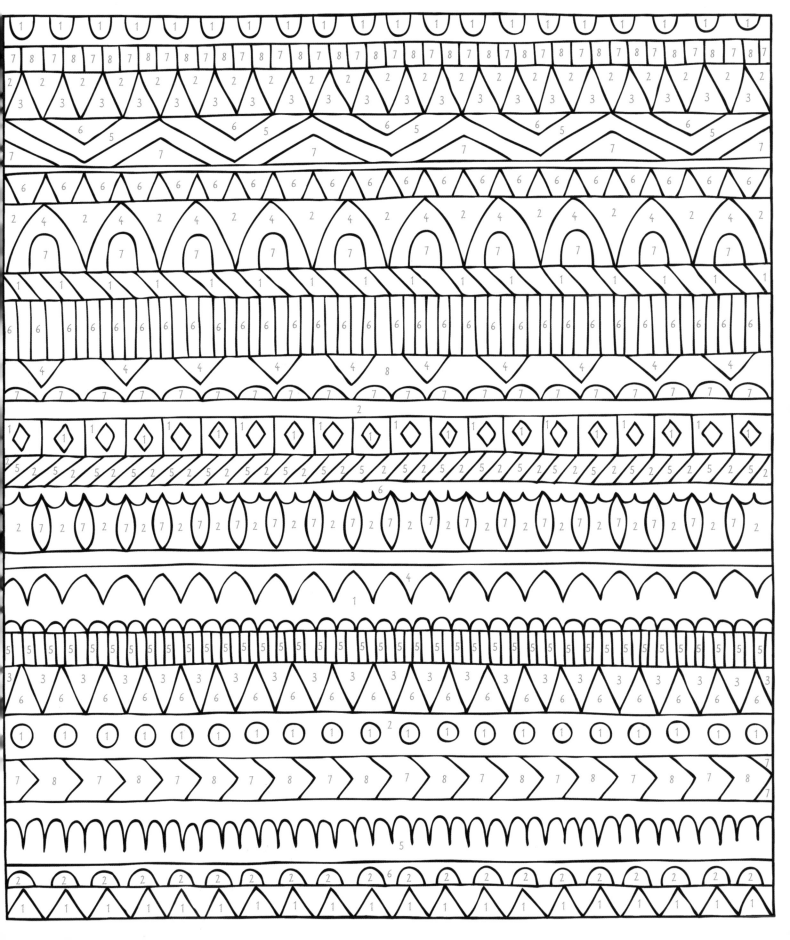

Color code

1 - orange   2 - brown
3 - yellow   4 - turquoise
5 - light blue   6 - dark blue
7 - gray   8 - red

Color code
1 - red   2 - yellow   3 - orange

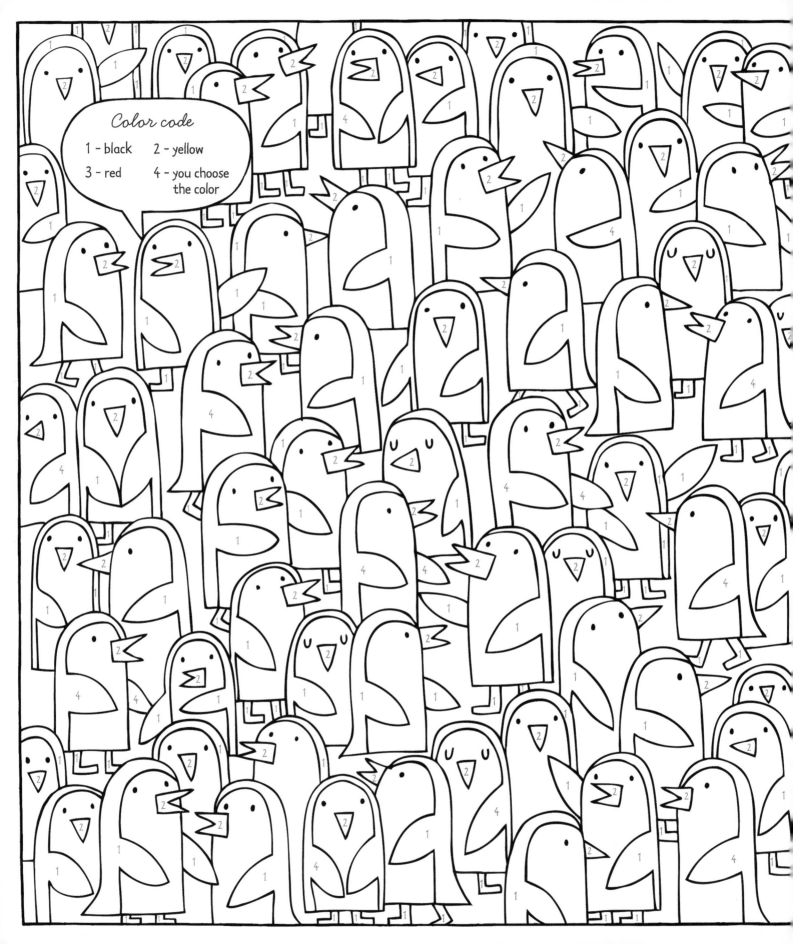

Color code

1 - black   2 - yellow
3 - red   4 - you choose
               the color

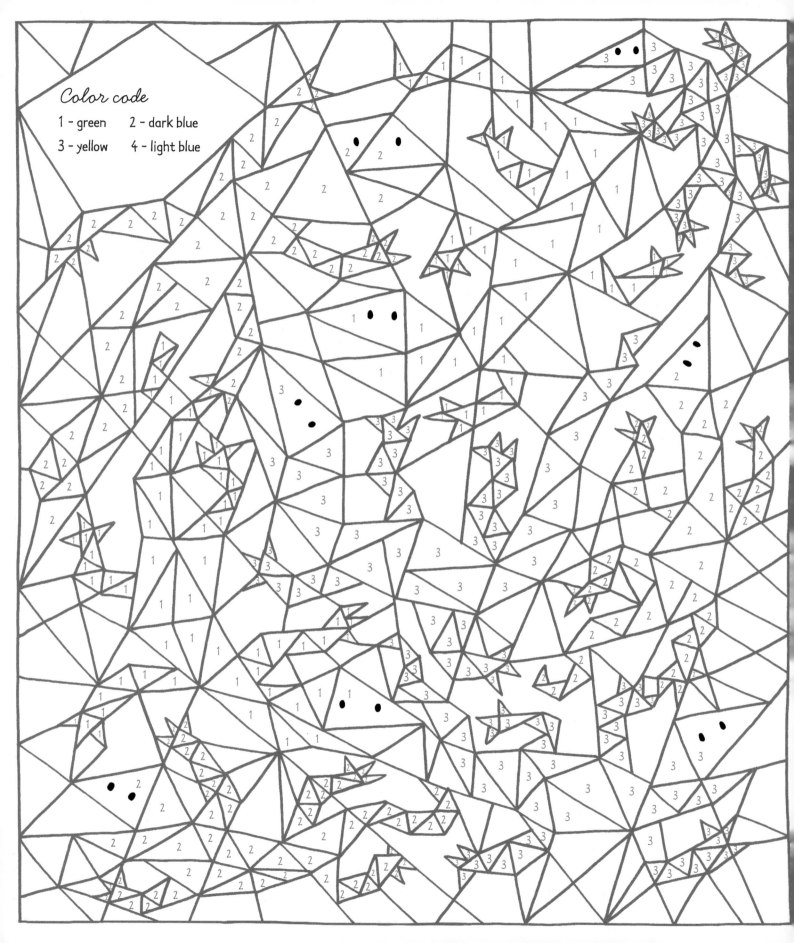

Color code

1 - green   2 - dark blue

3 - yellow   4 - light blue

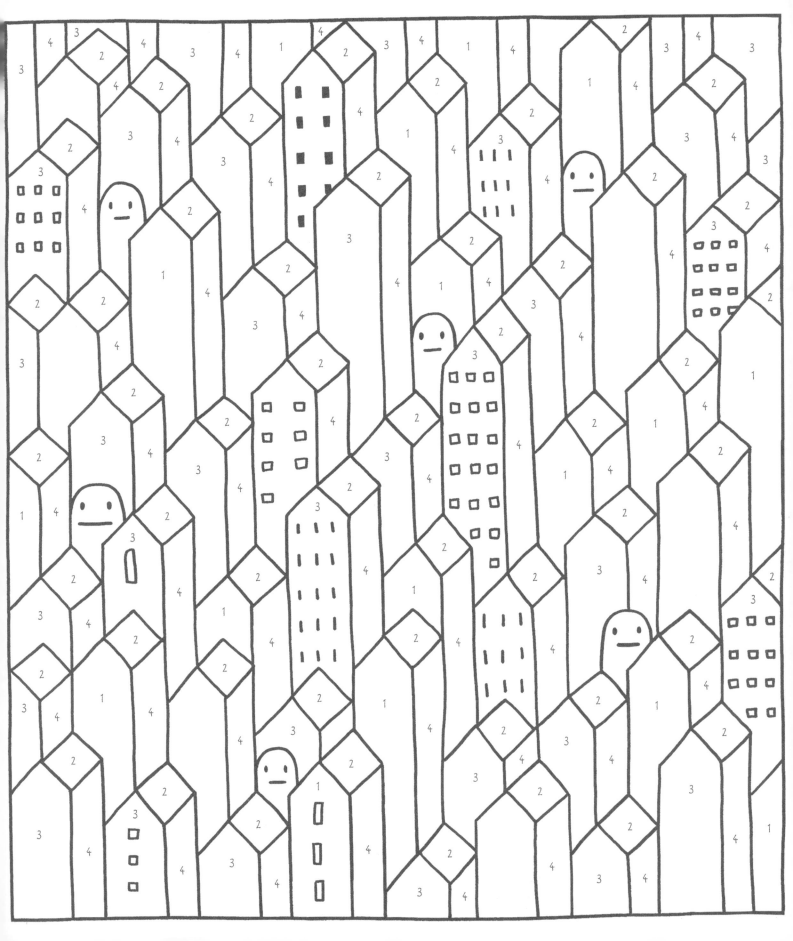

Color code

1 – red   2 – yellow
3 – pink   4 – purple
5 – dark blue   6 – green
7 – light blue

Color code

1 - red   2 - yellow

3 - blue   4 - turquoise

5 - green   6 - orange

Color code
1 - blue   2 - gray
3 - yellow   4 - red

Color code

1 - dark blue
2 - light blue
3 - turquoise
4 - orange

These two pages look identical but you may be surprised when you color them in.

Color code

1 - turquoise   2 - yellow
3 - dark blue   4 - orange
5 - red

When you've colored in this page, spot the different shapes and patterns you've created.

Color code

1 – red   2 – light blue
3 – purple   4 – yellow
5 – pink   6 – orange
7 – green

Color code   1 - black   2 - red   3 - light blue   4 - yellow   5 - green   6 - orange   7 - dark blue

Color code

1 – turquoise   2 – dark blue
3 – purple   4 – light blue
5 – black   6 – orange
7 – pink

Color code

1 - red   2 - pink   3 - orange
4 - yellow   5 - light green   6 - dark green
7 - light blue   8 - dark blue

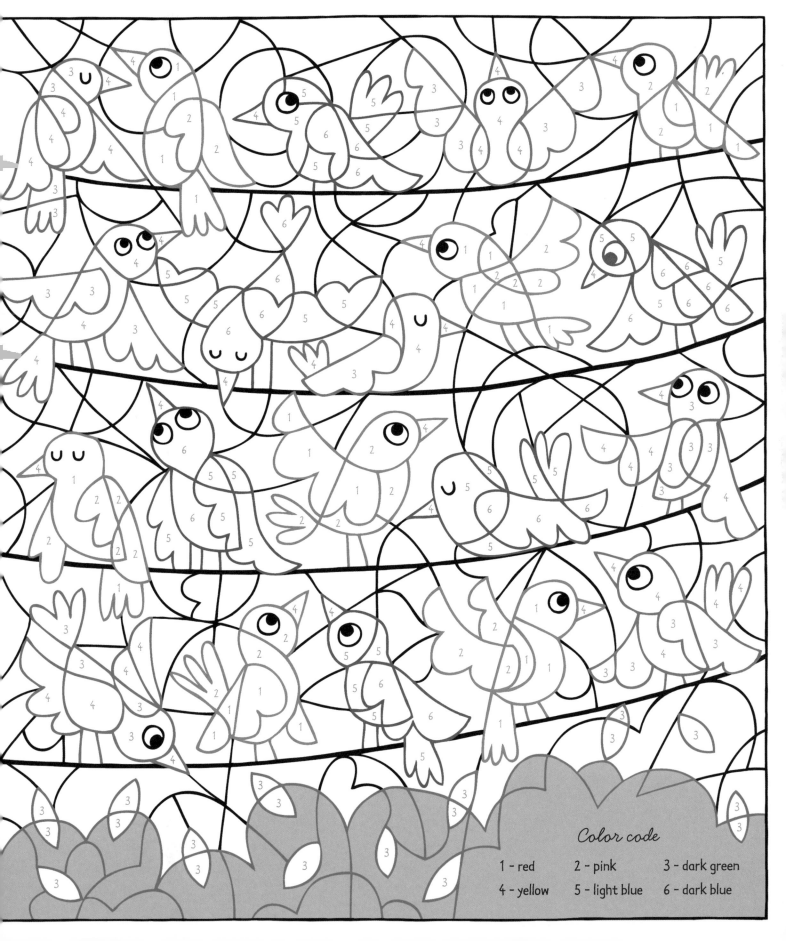

Color code

1 - red   2 - pink   3 - dark green

4 - yellow   5 - light blue   6 - dark blue

Color code

1 - orange
2 - yellow
3 - pink
4 - red
5 - dark blue
6 - light green
7 - light blue
8 - dark green
9 - purple

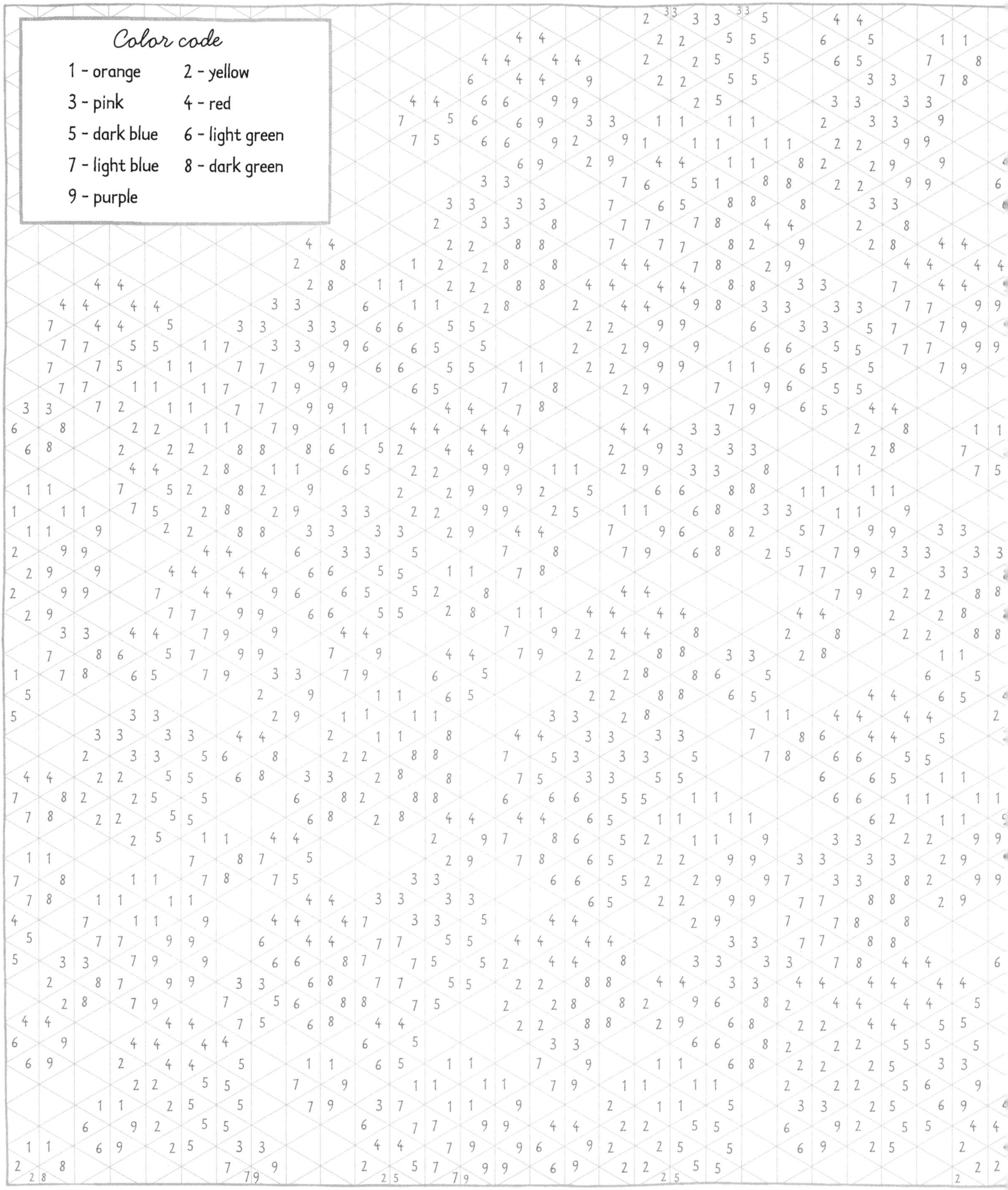

Color code
1 - red   2 - orange
3 - yellow   4 - light blue
5 - light green   6 - dark blue
7 - dark green

Color code

1 - yellow   2 - red   3 - light blue
4 - light green 5 - pink   6 - dark green
7 - dark blue 8 - orange   9 - black

Color code

1 - red   2 - yellow
3 - green   4 - dark blue
5 - light blue   6 - orange

These patterns on these pages look identical but you'll get different results when you color them.

Color code

1 - red   2 - yellow

3 - green   4 - dark blue

5 - gray

When you've colored in this page, spot the different shapes you've created.

Color code   1 - light green   2 - red   3 - turquoise   4 - yellow   5 - orange   6 - black   7 - pink

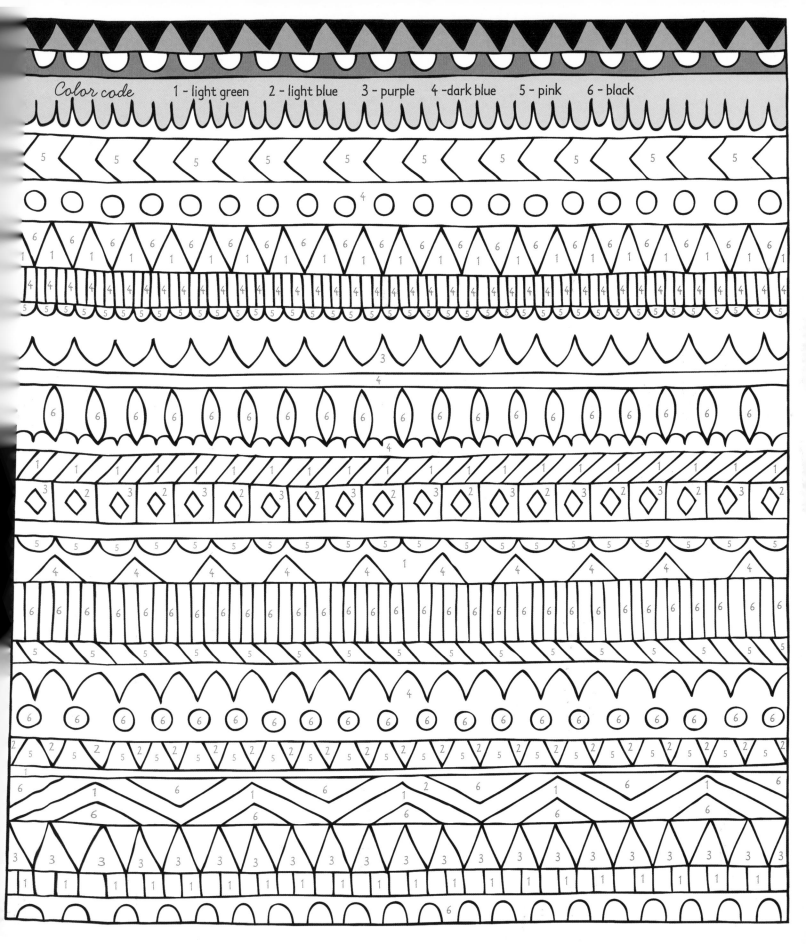

Color code   1 - light green   2 - light blue   3 - purple   4 -dark blue   5 - pink   6 - black

Color code

1 - dark blue   2 - yellow

3 - green   4 - orange

5 - red